CW00431327

The Mou
Drew

Ellie Coxall

BookLeaf
Publishing

Presentation by *BookLeaf Publishing*

Web: www.bookleafpub.com

E-mail: info@bookleafpub.com

ISBN: 9789357697200

First edition 2023

DEDICATION

Benjamin Jonah - an unanticipated galaxy.

ACKNOWLEDGEMENT

"With freedom, books, flowers, and the moon, who could not be happy?" - Oscar Wilde

Thank you, reader for buying, borrowing, or skimming through this little book of mine! The Mountains We Drew came quite spontaneously this year. I didn't expect to be writing one again so soon after The Wooden Balloon, but here we are.

To my best friends, Elise & Gwen. Thank you for inspiring me, encouraging me, giving me many cuddles and hugs, for having a snack box, for supporting me through many cups of coffee and for generally just being you two! So much love!

BookLeaf Publishing, thank you so much for this opportunity again! I'm so honoured to have worked with you.

To mum, I'm sorry you had to endure my frustration through the last few chapters of this book. Thank you for everything you do for me!

To Vineyard53 Chester, thank you for your endless kindness, love, faith and so many hugs! I'm so truly blessed to have you.

"Whatever you do, work at it with all your heart, as working for the Lord, not for human masters, 24 since you know that you will receive an inheritance from the Lord as a reward. It is the Lord Christ you are serving". - Colossians 3 23-34 (NIV)

PREFACE

Writing, releasing, designing and publishing a book will always be my greatest and proudest achievement! I'm so incredibly lucky to be in this position again with BookLeaf Publishing, almost a year later, to be holding book number two. My twelve year old self would be ecstatic! Thank you for picking up this book, whether you're a friend or an avid poetry reader, I appreciate you.

The Mountains We Drew

I lift my chin so my eyes can see in line with the
mountain peaks
My jaw mimicking the frame of the climb
Wind strong and rain weak
The avalanche about to chime

Peaks persevering perfectly
Stronghold together alongside lakes
Waves contributing harmlessly
To the pain the hail makes

Lakes the giver of fertility
Empty roads preparing the way
Mountains the voice of serenity
I kneel, worship and obey

These are the mountains we drew
These are the mountains you coloured
Oh father if only we knew
How much you had suffered

I drew these mountains with chalk and with sin
You painted these peaks with freedom and love
May I seek to always find the colour you are in
May I always fix my eyes on what's above

The peak that I am standing on
I won't be for much longer
For Lord I know there is no one
That is indeed stronger

The peak that I am standing on
I will stumble and fall
My footing will be gone
Yet you have already paid it all

I no longer need to worry about injury
About life or about death
Even on this rock blistery
I do not lose my breath

You've done this all before
you've seen the depth of the drop
and yet you preached on this uneven floor
you've reached the very top

I stand here as a witness
Like others previously
Appreciating your forgiveness
Almost immediately

I have seen and sensed grief
More than I thought I could bear
But there has been no disbelief
Because I know the weight that you care

I lift my chin so my eyes can see in line with the
mountain peaks
They persevere through thy treacherous weather
So when I hear on the peak that the wind that speaks
It will be the weather that we have persevered
through together

I provide the lead and the ink
But you have made me from clay
The gray scale in the rain sinks
Your colour will reflect what you would say

These are the mountains that we drew
The mountains we drew together
For everything and everyone I have I thank you
For I know I can brave this weather

Artist

She never considered herself an artist. She knows her reds from her blues, the primary and secondary colours, and how to draw a fairly decent flower or two, but she never really thought enough to label herself as an 'artist'. She grew up with highly creative people around her. She was always filled with inspiration or encouragement from them. Her dad was an artist. A pretty good one too. She has some of his paintings around her house, a vast swarm of delicate watercolour views by a riverbank and tiny white houses in a large field with long hairs of grass surrounding. Light greens burnt yellows and baby blues. Truly beautiful. She hopes to have her paintings sitting next to his on the wall one day, he would have liked that.

She's visited the Art Galleries around cities, swarmed away from the crowds of shopping bags, bowling alleys and overpriced restaurants. She finds her joy within the acrylic delicate brush strokes of a tired hand. She remembers circling the inside of a temple like building, expectant to see the dynamic and the disturbing trapped into a canvas.

Eventually, she opened by mind to the gallery walls, becoming pleasantly surprised with the distributed splashes of paint and detailed shiny oil that appeared on the paper hanging on the long-overstretched walls.

Paper ranging from seventeenth century canvas to the twenty first century promotion banners disregarded her interest. The walls varied from tiny flowers in a box print to large, over sized watercolour – portraits of women tensed up within a fraction of their being. The eyes of the painted dolls a deep blue colour, it was bleeding from the overuse of water, and it seeped into her man-made oily skin. Her art never quite compared.

The four walls of the gallery grew as she continued her path up the old staircases, steps dressed in a white marble with small specks of dirt in the corners. There were sculptures up the sides of what seemed like ancient Greeks. The engravement of the people were white, being surrounding in the background by a coat of the colour red, making the Greeks in their chitons of linen sitting on tables stand out even more than they might have intended. They seemed trapped, like the rest of the art here. She didn't want her art to be trapped.

Do you think it's better to be the artist, or the art itself?

"The Only Tired I Was, Was Tired Of Giving In"

Alabama 1955.

The sky was blue that it always has been, but the clouds seemed different. They seemed more separated than they have been before, and the usual white fluffy colour was stained with a light grey. Rosa had just finished a full day of working in the department store, it was only the first day of December, but the Christmas decorations were already up, and the stands of present ideas, next year's calendars and festive candy were on show at the front of the window. Rosa was a fairly small woman, thin and pretty in the face. There were a pair of glasses that sat upon her nose, small fragile ones that slid down the bridge of her nose. She often had to push the middle back up again. Her hair was tied back into a small bun that was placed just above her neck, letting the cool afternoon breeze kiss the back of her skin.

There was only a couple of other people at the bus stop waiting. Both white men with sharp suits on. One had a large briefcase in his hand, clutching it so his knuckles turned pale. He yawned and checked his watch on his wrist, stretching his arm out so the sleeve on his blazer was tucked up a little bit. His yawn caught Rosa's eye and forced her to release a yawn also, she raised a hand to her mouth though unlike the gentleman. The other was staring down the road, in the predicted direction of the bus. He was propped up by his arm on the side of the bus shelter, his hand in his pocket with his other holding a similar briefcase to the other one, although he didn't have the same grip on

6

it. He had a pair a glasses on his nose too, but squarer and bolder than the dainty ones that Rosa had propped on her nose.

The bus eventually arrived at around three minutes after it said it would. It came down the road smoothly, and pulled up to the side of the curb, letting out a big breath of air as it stopped. The two white men entered the bus first and greeted the driver with the same 'hello', 'thank you' like every day. Rosa reached the floor of the bus and made her way down the small aisle. In the middle of the seats, there were the signs simply saying 'White' on a small professional cardboard sign. There were the normal two rows of seats and two places for people to sit either side. They had the horrible sticky leather laid them that became flimsy with age, slippery with wear and a fear that they were never cleaned. The front of the bus was all filled with white men and women, having two seats taken up by the gentlemen that Rosa had seen at the shelter. Their briefcases were sat on their knee flat, while one watched the view by the window and the other sneaked a peek over another man's shoulder to read the paper. Another debate over the leading role of Martin Luther King was emerging on page 4 again. Rosa resentment rose a little for those who protest as she walked past him and his newspaper. She made it to the last seat behind the white sign, the back of it, blank, stared at her. The fury inside her rose again a little, but she tried to distract herself by looking through the window. The other black person that she was sat next to was also watching the evening streets move at a fast pace and in a blur. The department store spun past her in a hurry. A wave of relief swept through Rosa as she could forget about the amount of work left to do and give it to tomorrow. One woman sat in front of her had her thumb stuck in the middle of a book to mark the page. Rosa tried to read the page that she was on, but the woman's shoulder was too broad and her height too high. She thinks it could have been a English war romance but it wasn't clear.

It wasn't that long that the bus came to a holt again, letting out another gasp of air. The bus was full now, which meant someone will have to stand. And everyone was aware that it legally would have to be a black person. Much to Rosa's dismay, another white man entered the bus and stepped up towards the driver. The city bus driver, managed to climb out of his seat from behind the bulky steering wheel and walked down the aisle with the white passenger following, making his way towards Rosa.

"Could you stand please" he asked, holding out a hand for them to follow to stand at the back of the bus. He grabbed the white sign and moved it over Rosa's head to the back of hers. Rosa's anger and frustration rose to the point where her fists became white and her legs became paralysed.

Lucas

The boy next door. The boy through the wall.

We shared a wall for 2 years and 1 month and 4 days, and yet we never spoke. The occasional nod was given and received.

I knew so much about Lucas. More than he would think I would know. But we never spoke in those 2 years, 1 month and 4 days.

Every misty morning of September and October, when I knew no one, Lucas began to be a familiar face at 7:45am at the bus stop. A constant. We would hunch in the depths of our coat, standing 6 feet apart, social distancing before social distancing was even a thing. I knew his wardrobe fairly well, so I could recognise when a new coat had been purchased, or a new pair of shoes. My parcels used to arrive at his door, and he would take them in for me, so I'm pretty sure he knew the extent of my wardrobe too considering how many of those parcels were ASOS. We'd get on the same bus. Sit apart and say nothing. It was like that for 2 years and 3 weeks.

One morning he didn't turn up to the bus stop on time, or at all. And I knew why. I heard pain through my wall the night before. It echoed into my room and stained the paint on the wall. I listened closely, pressing my ear to the wall to hear panic. I felt panic, and I felt concern. 26 minutes later Lucas was in a wheelchair being taken in an ambulance for suspected sepsis. I was looking through my mum's bedroom window to see him go, she had heard the pain too and awoke. She also had the view from the front. Even though he wasn't really my friend, I cared for him. It hurt me that he was in pain. I wish we could have shared it, so it wasn't all on him. I said a big prayer.

That's why he wasn't at the bus stop the next day. I knew why. I don't know if he knew that I knew. I don't know if he felt my concern.

We never spoke about it.

I baked his family cookies for Christmas. My mum wrote the card, and I delivered cinnamon men (I didn't have any ginger) and passed them on to his mum. Lucas ate the cookies. I think he liked them.

Our dogs were best friends. Their noses used to connect between a hole in the fence in our tiny gardens, our mums used to come out to say hello while they were at it. Used to talk about me and Lucas and what we were doing or how we were doing. Our conversations were never told through ourselves, but through our mums.

I met his girlfriend briefly. She was also a brief girlfriend. She walked to his after college sometimes, about 8 feet in front of me. I think she thought that I was following her.

We've spoken now. Myself and Lucas. And I left Manchester to move to Wales. I accidentally ordered another parcel to our old address, so had to come back for it while we were seeing friends there. I knocked on his door like I'd done a few times before. This time, however, he answered the door.

"Hi, um, I'm here for the parcel. I'm Ellie, I used to live next door"

He smiled at me.

"Oh yeah, I remember, I'm Lucas". I already knew that.

For the next 13 minutes we talked about where and what he was studying at university, how he didn't enjoy college and his favourite cereal.

"So, Lucas, are you still studying Law?" I asked, just as he filled his mouth with a mountain of Cheerio's on his spoon. His sister was busy searching around the house for my parcel.

"Nah" he mumbled, trying to chew his cereal as fast as possible. "I dropped it, I'm now doing maths".

"Ew" I accidentally said out loud, a little too quick. He laughed.

"Yeah, I often get that reaction" he chuckled. I laughed with him awkwardly.

"What about you? Did you go and do music? I used to hear your guitar
sometimes through the wall, you were really good" he asked. I paused.

He remembered my music. He listened. He cared.

"Ah I didn't realise you could hear me, thank you" I laughed a little back. I was astonished.

"Sorry, I hope that didn't sound creepy" he laughed.

"No, not at all" I replied, "I'm studying Creative Writing now. In Bangor".

"Ah okay, cool!" he said, stuffing another mouthful of cereal in and looking behind him where his sister was coming out of the utility room with my parcel. Then we said our goodbyes. For good.

Looking back, it would have been so much easier to just be friends with him for those 2 years, 1 month and 4 days.

Strawberries & Cream

She was heavy,

Small but heavy.

Oddly shaped, flat on one side, and curvy on the other

Red & cream.

Strawberries and cream.

You can see the cream swirled into the berries, and where the cream has rejected the berry

ah to be the berry

Maybe she wasn't strawberries and cream.

She didn't taste sweet

Looked kind of rough.

Tasted kind of rough.

The stream of cream made the strawberry scream to the sides

A river of cream left in the middle

With a scar running through it

And tiny holes in the strawberry

Seedless

Mislead us

It's not strawberries and cream anymore

Nor a raspberry ripple

But the light dunes of sand amongst the fiery red ground

With dusty pink grains swept to the side

The soft formation of the mountains begins to show

With a crack in the peak to show where to go

To the birds that fly ahead

And nest in the tiny holes of the red sands

All this I hold in my hands

Right before the sunset lands

Seeming to Sink

Earth seems to sink from
Weight.
Wait.
Soil too weak to uphold the green
green was drowning
strands were drowning
I was drowning
land was breaking
sun was breaking
I was drowning
I was breaking
sun was drowning
birds in mourning
In the morning.
I was sinking
feet were sinking

In the land coral of earth
Small villages crushed
Leather killer
Blood on boots
Blood on my hands
Blood on the spot
Out. Be dammed.

Moss is the coral
Bugs, beetles, bookworms
are fish

Cold is biting
Freezing wires under the skin
In the brain
In the vision
In the bones
In the veins
In the fingers
In my breath.

two orange leaves.
two birds leave.

Silence for September

I leave the door unlocked. Like I always do, leaving my house and possessions into the hands of God and fate. Once I hear the handle of the door shoot upwards brushing past all the other locks on the way I tend not to think about it again. I drop the keys into the side pocket of my coat and turn my back to the door, looking at the road ahead.

I leave the depression, stress, anxiety, fear, and bad attitude on my bed, and just take myself out of the house. Like I'm out of my own brain. There are still a few crumbs left of anxiety left scattered around in my mind, but I'll try my hardest to brush them to the side.

I proceed to reach the first road, as the stones crunch below my feet, cracking their bones as I walk over them. The trees seem annoyingly peaceful in the breeze, as they dance according to the chimes that the wind gives out. I'm jealous of the wind. The wind is free and moves at its own pace, with no responsibility. I can hear the wind whistle through a whole that was pierced through our plastic bins, singing or screaming I couldn't tell which one. It was pointless to stick around to find out.

The trees are dressed in green with fragments of orange, meaning that autumn is sneaking in and September is about to be forgotten. I take a couple of minutes silence to remember September. They look so alive. I'm jealous of the trees. They stand tall too, showing their power to every other plant that surrounds them. They even intimidate me a little, feeling like I was one of the weeds that invades the path. I carry on walking, making my way off the dried bones of stones onto the pavement that lies next to the next road. I hate the hum and roar of cars next to me. I'm not jealous of the cars. They're too many of them, and they disrupt and harm the earth. I think if I were a tree, I would feel the same.

Roundabouts, Roads, Rain, Rainbows, Rocks. I choose the letter 'R' to ground myself with as I walk, so my mind wouldn't wander and increase the size of the crumbs left in my mind.

I finally reach the sea. Deep, distorted, dark blue, desolate, desirable. I next choose the letter 'D'. I'm also jealous of the sea. It's like the wind, but you can see it, and you can float in it. You can still touch the wind, but it's not the same. I love the current. It creates a little road where the birds can float without doing any work. I'm also jealous of the birds.

Walking back, I could only think of the mind diseases that I left in my room, and the peace that has slipped into my mind when walking. The handle locked up again as I walk back into the house and into my room. But the room isn't as cold and dim as when I left it, and the anxiety has left.

if.

if she is your sunshine, what am i? your moon?

no. you are an unanticipated galaxy.

Earth

The 5am sun starts to peek over the top of the mountains, to the right of the van. When the sun hit the top of the peak, the orange beams spread out like arms that engulf the night sky that once covered the blanket above. I can't see her as well when the orange light hits, that's when she and the van moves around the most.

The sun hits her window slow but harshly, sometimes blinding her eyes, but they make the blue stand out more. She dresses in the same outfit as she did yesterday. A pair of stretched black leggings that are too long for her. The bottoms are rolled up showing a bit of her tanned ankle at the bottom, the sides of the material clear with no brands. No tick or stripes of the adidas, she doesn't give in to societies expectations of being young. Another reason that I love her.

A plain white t shirt accompanies her leggings, slimming down her waist slightly, and then hanging a washed blue denim shirt partnered over the top. A chain of two necklaces sit lightly on her chest. One a baby pink swirl pattern on a plectrum from a guitar. She still plays where she can, it used to be a full-time hobby until she discovered me. Her fingertips are still pretty tough and hard though from the pressure of the strings though. The other necklace is a plain cross. Aside from the magazines, this is her most precious item. She only became religious a few years ago I think, but it seems to give her more strength and ability to carry on every morning. Especially since her grandfather died. I believe this is a big reason why she is here to help me. I've never seen her pray though.

Back on the road she goes. The van wobbles about a bit but it's steady enough to get her where she wants to go. She has a lake view spread out on her dashboard, a double page spread. The lake is blue and has a layer of shine over the top like sugar, it glistens in the sun that has again reached the top of the mountain peak. The mountains are in the midst of the autumn again, with the bursts of yellow, orange, and red popping out from every corner of its rock heart. The forest that surrounds the lake has been painted in the same fire colours, hosting homes to animals like bears and deer. The lake is called Vermillion Lake I read on the creased page, a Canadian mountain and lake range. Her shoulders are hunched over the wheel while squinting her eyes to find the signpost that should be fast approaching. Her glasses are somewhere around the van, wherever she decided to sleep last. Her excitement builds, but the image in the page deceives her.

She sees that I am dying. And that I'm broken. The drive on the way to the lake wasn't what she was expecting. The sides of the road were supposed to be highlighted in forest green, mint, and sage. Instead they were dusted with death and the twigs as fragile as a glass jar.

She slid the door of the van outward and to the side and jumped outwards on to the dead grass. Her gaze to the mountains was one of pure devastation. She continued down the path that wasn't really a path, it was a space in the middle of a haunting forest graveyard.
0
The stumps of the trees drowned into the rotting soil. There was no real sight anymore that this was a forest, no animals or plants dared to set up a home there, as there was already very few places to build one, let alone only a few animals left. The ground on which she stepped on was dark and

crisp, no moisture to left to even steal a drop of its sickly, dark blood. She was steady in her step, afraid of the ground being so broken that she would fall right through it and be trapped within the skeletons of the leaves and bones of the twigs.

She imagined inhaling the soil. The rock-hard pieces hitting the back of her throat as the small stones trickled down her throat like saliva, her breath slowly but harshly, being taken away from her.

She didn't fall through; I wouldn't let that happen to her.

The lake in front of her had dried up completely, revealing a few more hundred hidden skeletons of fish that once fed families of bears and birds. None of which can be seen now.

You see she goes on these adventures to these places that she discovers in her magazines and is always struck by the canvas of death before her. People used to care about the wellbeing of me, I offered them everything that God intended me too, but they took advantage of me. People like David, Greta and now Alexa they try and save me and warn other people.

She continued around the side of the pit, walking heavy footed to gain stability under foot, the cracking of the spines of the sticks below hitting sparks on the bottom of her shoes. Her hand grazed over the top of the dead stumps of the trees and stroked them with care with the tip of her thumb. A few strands of her hair wafted down to her face, the blue in her eyes being split in two by the line. The smell of the wind was potent and strong. The smell was smoking and rich from the wildfires that it burned her nose slightly.

Another crack echoed in the distance behind her. She was sure there mustn't be anyone else here, why would there be? The hair that once covered her eye slightly whipped round harshly forcing the hair to hit the side of her cheek. Eyes wide and mouth slightly open, she removed her hand from the stump and slowly straightened her back to stand tall. The fear immediately crept in, she was not prepared to meet another person, or animal or whatever it is. She was a naive 20-year-old, vulnerable and dumb at most, her mother liked to remind her persistently. Another big reason why she is probably doing this. That house was toxic.

A figure moved through the trees in front of her, a distance that she was safe for now, but there were no tall trees to hide behind anyway. The figure was human like, there's no doubt about it. It was also tall, but their shoulders were bent over slightly in weakness, an old figure perhaps. Her breathe quickly became fast paced, but still remaining invisible in the air. Remember that I'm dying and what the cause might be, the sun has warmed up since you last saw it.

The cracks and spark under her feet mellowed in the slow pace she took, moving closer to the figure. Fear suddenly escaped her as she realised who it was, well she didn't know them yet, but they seemed harmless.

A older man, around maybe the age of 60 to 65, was crouched on his knees on the floor, the knees of his jeans were not even a little dirty, but the end of his checked sleeves were wet

with dirt. His eyes and his hands were cupped on a little baby bird that lay stuck between the rotten twigs from the ground, a small little chirp entered the air every few seconds. His hands were old, tired, and tanned, with the

23

cracks of his nails and skin folded and creased in with dirt. His top half was slightly round, but his olive-green puffer jacket filled most of his waist so who was she to know. The shirt underneath was a red checked shirt, the top two buttons undone. It hadn't occurred to her how close she had gotten to the man until he had made eye contact with her. His face was slightly tanned too, with specks of wrinkles and lines that run through the course of his skin. You can see where he smiled, the lines playfully jumping above his cheeks, navigating the road of skin up to his eyes. He didn't greet her with a smile though, but with a look of utter confusion and amazement. Even the little, tiny bird that had just been granted freedom from the twigs looked at her astonishingly, nesting again in the fingertips of the man.

Say something. Anything. I was desperate for her to have help, after all she can't save the world by herself, now can she? Please. Say something.

"Hey there, sorry I- I didn't mean to scare you" she said timidly.

That will do. Thank you.

The man stood tall from the ground and came to the same level as her, stumbling a little as his legs locked back into place.

"No that's okay don't worry, are you okay? Are you lost?" he replied, looking concerned for her. The bird was still nestled in his hands.

"No I sorry I just came to explore a bit, It's looking quote scarce around here isn't it" she looked around, her hair in a loose high pony tail that flipped around as she looked.

"Definitely not, we're only to blame though. Oh but it used to be so beautiful"

"Only some of us, some hearts are more sympathetic to nature" she shrugged as she spoke, making sure that she didn't seem so forward with the guy.

I'm so proud of her.

"Very true young lady, what's your name?" he smiled at her courage to a stranger. An old stranger if I must say.

"Alexa, and you?"

"Graham. So how did you find us?"

"I followed the directions from an old magazine I had in my van, but i- wait 'us?'.
There's more of you?" She was just as concerned as he was about her.

"See that cabin up there, by the edge of the ditch?" He pointed to an old medium sized shack that was stood stable in the middle of where all the dead tree trunks were. The cabin itself was still in very good shape, the windows were big and illuminated with light, and the balcony and the decking still seemed strong. It looked lonely though. It was sitting amongst a graveyard of a dead earth.

Sitting on my grave. Sitting on my dying body. Yet it was the only thing keeping me alive.

"Is that where you live?" she asked, her eyes still transfixed on the cabin.

"It's where we live, the community" He found it quite amusing to watch her be surprised by something that was so ordinarily normal a few years ago.

She looked back at Graham; her face confused yet again.

"The community? What do you mean?"

Graham fidgeted on his leg a little, still cupping the small bird in his hands.
It's hard to stand on my corpse. You would wobble too if you were there.

"Well after all the cases and deaths of Coronavirus and the amount of people that died from the dramatic climate change from like 30 years ago, it wiped out a good chunk of our population here. So we decided to live all together to keep each other safe. We came to join with the animals, but of course they were all wiped out too, along with their homes. We had no technology and no signal anyway, and the roads looked the same than the soil so we were lost. We stayed and set up a cabin to try and salvage what we could. As you can see, we haven't really made much of a dent in the case."

His face dropped slowly as he kept talking, the navigation lines by his eyes were drooping. I could see Alexa's spirit go with it.

"But at least you are actually doing something! How long have you all been rebuilding?" she said with great disturbance and concern

"A good 20 years now, took us a while to get rid of all disease and pollution that we could with very few – well with little stuff"

"And this is all you have to show for it?!" She turned around again behind her in disbelief, looked into the deep abyss of my spine. My dying dry bones.
She didn't mean for it to come out so blunt and disrespectful, it just came out.

"Well not exactly, this was one of the most damaged areas of wildfires, so we had to be careful with the smoke for years with some of our older folk. Trust me, it's not all this bad"

Her heart was breaking, I could feel it.

"Would you like to meet the community?" he asked gently. The bird was still nestled. I wonder when was the last time that that little bird ever got nestled or cared for.

Well I wouldn't know, would I?

"Very much" she replied with a small smile.

It was a much shorter walk than she anticipated. They walked straight through where the ditch of the lake once was. The ground was dry and cracked and the skeletons of the animals still rotting in the dead soil. The bird woke up every now again from the shock of Grahams heavy footprints. He had a slight limp as he walked, she could see some part of his leg when the warm wind hit the edge of his trouser leg, revealing a large scar imprinted upon his skin. She doesn't wish to know where it's from or how he got it.

When they reached the cabin, a few of the other members of the community came out of the shack, and some from around the back of the garden. How can there be a garden? Maybe they mean graveyard.

The cabin that they called home was a short long hut made entirely of plastic. Plastic bottles, bags, cups, trays. They were melted into one another to create a big blocks of bricks. You could see an array of labels that had been on the plastics, like the faint outline of the words ready salted and sunflower oil were visible on the front few steps.

Some of the community flooded out of the door. When I say door I mean it was a curtain of shredded plastic. There were only a few that she saw, they weren't expecting a visitor after all.

They looked at her with pure confusion. Some came rushing to her, some slowed down. It was like an apocalypse, hungry for brains, or hungry for any other human interaction. Her fists clenched up and she took her steps easy. I could smell her fear from my grave.

She wasn't sure how to react, it didn't look like they meant any harm but, I feared for her too. I feared for them all, they are my last hope.

"This is Alexa"

An older woman walked up to her, with her hands stretched out and placed her hands in hers. She had a mother's touch within her, and she gave her mothers love out to everyone and anyone who needed it. Claudia that was her name. Wife to Graham. Her hands were soft and skinny, with the same folds and wrinkles that Graham had. Her eyes were so full of soul and spirit, it was so easy to fall into them. The same navigation lines that Graham also had on his face were the same as hers, the roads leading to her deep pools of green.

Another middle-aged guy walked up to her too, smiled and carefully took the tiny bird out of grahams hands into his own dark chocolate hands. There weren't folds or creases like Grahams or Claudia's, He was tall and dark, is height towering above Alexa.

"This is Daniel, my son." Claudia said wrapping her olive tanned arm around him.
Alexa smiled and shook his hand. She was still in disbelief of where she was and who she was with. An hour ago she was by herself in her van looking for hope. I don't think she actually think she would find it.

Prickly Politics

Borey Tory Pecks Pretentious People. Prickly
Politics. Dare To Boot Boris. Poor Politics. Poor
People.
Take Proper Breaks Boris. KitKat.
                                    To Kool To Be Devouring
KitKats. Posh Politician.
Don't Take Personally.
Don't Take.
Takes Time.
Do Good Boris. Do Better Boris. Please Do. Tick.
Tick. Pick.
Downing
      going
          Down. Take Parties, Beers, Peers, Tears Back.
Boris Behaved Badly.
Politics Boris Picks, Tories Ticks, Downing
                                          Down, Games
Drained.
                                          People D
R A I

N

E

D
Great British Bake Off. Banana Bread Takes The
Biscuit. Boris Took The Banana Bread Took The

Biscuit. TOOK BANANA BREAD TO POLITICAL
PARTIES.
Took Politics Too Personally.
Took Politics Too Pleasingly.
Took Politics, People, Privilege Too Prematurely. Too
Perilously.

Earth vs Economics

"Gee, I hope it does collapse, because then I can go in
and buy NOTHING
WILL BE S A V E D WI T H O U T some and make
some money."

Well, it did collapse.

IT IS BEST TO BEGIN WITH business, by the way.

THE FACT Nine million people -- nine million
people lost their jobs.

I think it's real.

T H I S I S Y O U R I N V I T A T I O N T O LE
A D WI T H LIGHT .

I did not.

Y O U WERE B O R N T O BE FRIENDS O F
T H E PRECIOUS GR O U N D

I did not.

A IR. TIME. N OW I S A LL WE H A V E LEFT

I do not say that.

HOLDING THE WORLD IN OUR HAN
D S .

I think science is real.

THIS IS THE MOST IN CONVENIEN
T TRUTH TO HONOUR THE LAND, A
IR. SKY

And I think it's important that we grip this and
deal with it

[interruption]

OUR DAY IS OLDER THAN IT USED
TO BE

never going back to what got us in trouble in the first
place.

COME, LE A D I N G LIGHTS.

She talks about solar panels.

YOU WERE B O R N TO BE CREATORS OF
A POSSIBLE FUTURE.

Why are you just thinking about-

THE TRUTH WILL NOT LEAVE WITH
OUT YOU

I will bring -- excuse me

H E A V Y T H O U G H I T MA Y BE

30 years

LE A N I N G U PO N Y O U .

Are you listening?

Mr. Trump?

Carriage A

I made it just to the minute. The process of running for a train was always a form of exercise that I so adamantly try to avoid, but there come some mornings where time gets a little ahead of you in the race. I didn't appreciate the test this morning.

I'm dressed well, smart most would say. My differentiation in jobs calls for a differentiation in wardrobe, and I'm glad that mine can cater well for me.

The rush of adrenaline that has seeped through the skin of sweat in present, is not well received. The stands of hair that were freshly tamed this morning into a neat straight drop, has become a little wavy as I sit, breathe, calm and alter myself.

On my way from one responsibility to the other, the sea is a constant. Eighteen minutes into my weekly commute, the water comes in to greet me. Waves manoeuvre through the rocks, a business in their daily commute that looks peaceful to the eye and would sound peaceful to the ear. It may be a frantic search for direction in the lost current.

My current, an electrical one in Carriage A is not peaceful. Others on their way to their work, a matter of differentiation or not, it seems that most maybe don't commute to work quite as far as I do on a Wednesday morning. Elderly couples, elderly singles, families, single parents, school kids, school teachers, book readers, book writers, social media swipers, earphone isolates, the sleepers, Netflix catchups, downloaded podcasts, loud public facetime calls, bugs, viruses, mid November colds all fill up the carriages.

The sea a deep pearly blue that reflects the morning sky, only to be disturbed by construction workers on the sea front. The waves are travelling in a different direction to me, we're going against the grain. There's a soft blush pink that licks the horizon kept in the background of the morning clouds that hover above, yet they're too tired to push forward to get to the sea front. The waves sitting on top of the water are static. My eyesight has always been poor so they may have deceived me, I won't say 'has failed me' because they have done so much more than that.

The carriage leads me to grassy lands carved and tangled between the railway tracks, getting harshly beaten by the wheels and the hot wind that travels beneath carriage A. They looked frazzled.

The sun on the other side of the carriage making an appearance through the clouds that have gathered over the mountains, desperate to be met with my eye for a second and make it into the pages of this chapter. I will let it. The sun is squinting, narrow and squashed in its frame, but pressed up against the reflection of the window that sits next to me. If not concentrating enough, I'll lose focus and understanding of where the sun is truly placed.

Carriage A brings a comfort in my relationship with time. I've left my responsibilities in destination A, and I haven't yet arrived at my destination B, I'm travelling through time, in time to gather time to replace the time this week that I have not had. At some point here, through this hour commute, myself and time meet, and we make peace. Until next Wednesday.

I meet Carriage A again in the evening. It's different to the morning. There's more weakness in my eyes and more fatigue in my head. I'm still in the midst of my travelling relationship with time, but I have less energy than previously to take in elements around me. The glass is black and dark next to me, small specks of light reappearing and disappearing. Within the stops every now and again, shadowed cold figures in big coats, fluffy hats and scarves, bundle by the door of Carriage A to attempt to ensure their seat. Yet there are some leave Carriage A and instantly leave the warmth provided, in one step onto the platform as they pull up their coats close to their chin.

My mind is too far gone, too foggy to keep thinking. So, for now, I leave these thoughts of Carriage A, in Carriage A.

I was told.

I was told to always wear a dress on special
occasions, so I didn't look like a boy
I was told to put down the toy car that my brother
was playing with
I was told about death too early on and how it's okay
if I should need to cry
I was told to be a big girl and not cry when I fell over
and cut my knee
I was told
I was told
I was told
I was told.

And that's just childhood. You're constantly told to
not be someone or to be associated with them,
sometimes that being the opposite sex. Or rather
don't look like the opposite sex. Growing up in this
way is damaging for who?

I was told not to wear my hair far back because it
made me look bald
I was told stand tall and not slouch
I was told I wasn't smart enough to pass physics
I was told that I shouldn't be a dancer because I was
too big
I was told that I should go and socialise more
I was told I need to stay in to study to be able to get a
future

I was told that I shouldn't dress so provocatively as a
Christian woman in a crop top
I was told to have my hair straight because my curly
hair was too crazy
I was told to leave my hair curly because it was
natural
I was told
I was told
I was told
I was told.
And that's just my teenage years. You're at your most
insecure when you're body is changing. You're aware
of how your body is changing, you don't need to be
reminded of that either.

I was told to put the paintbrush down because I was
wasting my time
I was told to put my writing pen down because I was
wasting my time
I was told that if I kept doing these things, I wasn't
going to be able to pay the bills
I was told to stay quiet during things that didn't
concern me
I was told to speak up for what I believe it
I was told to not to speak too loud in case I offended
someone
I was told to not walk home alone in the dark
I was told that I shouldn't be in a certain position
because I'm a woman
I was told I was asking for it
I was told
I was told

I was told
I was told.
And this is now adulting. You have more of an
understanding and a voice. Although apparently,
you're not allowed to use it at times. You sometimes
get shut down by men when you try and educate them
on female security.

I was told too much
I was told too little
I am telling you -

                        Actually, I was told I wasn't
allowed to tell you.

Love isn't

Love isn't

1.   convenient
2.   weak
3.   controlled
4.   a mistake
5.   meant to hurt
6.   forced
7.   clay
8.   compulsive
9.   closed to you
10.   what other people say it should be

Boat

Imagine yourself as a boat.
Either wooden, broken or new
Are you sunken, tired up or afloat?
What is so great about you?

Are you being used for good?
Or simply there for decoration
Is your purpose being misunderstood
Are you reading on the reflection?

Do you have tools?
To keep you moving and in direction
On the ocean, a river, whatever variety of pool
Do you have a certain section?

I think I am likely to be a canoe
It has so little to give
I can't be compared to him too
See the state in which I live

His is a big yacht
He travels with a certain speed
While he was gone, I think he forgot
The water which I bleed

I am attached to his side
I am damaged and quick to fail
Why does he have so much pride?
Did he not hear my sorrowful tale?

"I may be a big yacht, he said
But that doesn't equal to hierarchy
I think you'll find I'd rather be you instead
There are some aspects you don't see

I am owned by the rich
The powerful and the famous
But I am not used for importance in which
I am only here to "entertain us"

You are a boat in which people take joy
There means for your use are pure
You are on for people to employ
When there is a life you need to secure"

The Altar

Thy altar was sightly cluttered.
With candlesticks, communion cups, cushions, the
cross and Christ
A wooden cross hanging, memory of thou sacrifice
I sit gladly by thy throne

The font is near, stoned and painted in oat and
markings
Thy cup is empty
Bread and wine, body and blood give plenty
Sweetly bitter and stiff in texture

The cream stoned arches stand tall and together
Wide in their stance and sharp dominance
Submissive still to the glass mirrors exuberant
Glass mirrors submissive to thy carved aperture

The hierarchy at the altar is false
For these are objects from human hands
I beg you to not misunderstand
The reign of Christ at his altar

Within thy woodwork, candle wax and lecterns
are centuries of worship, work and willingness
appreciate what these hands have given us
to settle and serve at this altar

the choir stalls are low, rigid and creaky
the voices of those who have sung still chime
in melody, harmony, soprano and rhyme
we sing there still

thy church is not in a building
but is in thy people who come
in those there are some
who serve robed on thou altar

we are to bring everything to you
our struggle, spirit and sin
forgiveness in what we have been
thou take the load

above thy altar
above the hanging cross strong
the bottom of the boat of Noah was there all along
acting as a lid in the upside down

his boat covered in beams
the beams horizontal in place
curved and rounded in the just case
that a flood will fall from above

in the secret and the hidden
to the altar and look left
shows a way where the unbelievers slept
behind the pipes of the organ

they ignore Christ's song
they want no association
in the faithful dedication
that it takes to follow a leader

the organ wakes them every few hymns
but they cover thine ears
but the lord till hears
their secret inmost prayers

the pathway behind the altar
leads to the vestry
the vestry where the priest and maestri
pray before the preach

our prayer follows thou
no matter the distance from thy altar
the faith will not faulter
Jesus, his altar and I.

right guy

one of the most beautiful sounds in this world is
hearing your best friends heart be so full and
happy, when she's sharing it with the right guy.

The Sausage Roll

A seagull's eye is the pinnacle
For us to know who's the criminal
They feast their eye on the hot pie
His focus becomes invincible

You run knowing you'll lose
His pinch will leave a bruise
You hide the pastry knowing it's tasty
Crumbs are dropping onto your shoes

The seagull sits and waits
Hovering above the Menai Straits
He sees your reaction for him to take action
And flies towards you and your mates
The chase is on and quickly
You see an exit clearly
But the bird is too fast he swoops just past
Your pie in hand quite severely

You're determined to not let go
The pier creaks and bounces below
You pull in haste as the bird takes a taste
Off the top of the flaky crust dough

You're still holding on tight
Through this chaotic and amusing fight
the seagull takes a nip at your finger by the tip
and as you let go the sausage roll flies out of sight

the bird cries in jubilation
to show off his trophy in adoration
it was just that easy for the bird for the catch the greasy
sausage roll, a taste sensation

the guy and his mates are in despair
as they watch their lunch in the air
they walk away with the defeat of the day
regretting ever eating their hot lunch there.

Melatonin

buttons of purple jelly
encased in purple plastic
Dosed, dripped and dipped in melatonin
Urging, yearning and learning
That human mind has a jelly of its own course

Unlike a course of electric
They are in capable of such
Filled and empty with too much
Filled with feelings, thoughts, figuration's
Things for Friday things for Thursday
Empty with everyone, everything stored in
The eye, envy, every mistake, every
Conversation

I learn, yearn, earn and burn
For my mind of which He secured me with
In His will
To be calm.
For I wish the waves of worry, wavering
Choices, partial parts of wisdom to settle
And save
To be remembered another day where there
Wasn't war, worry, woes, weight, waiting

Advent

The cathedral where the candles lay and the choir
sang, where the people crowded and the corners
shadowed, where Christ was present and where the
church cat wandered, waited.
It seemed that peace had already arrived before we
came in. It was seated in every chair and rested on
every cushion.
 It waited with us.

The gifts for those of us that came through the door
were serve sheets, an unlit candle and a smile. We
took our gifts and seated ourselves on the chair's
peace had reserved.
And still, we waited.
When it was time angels echoed in a corner voice is
soaring passing our hearts with its awe. the angels
after a few minutes, stopped as an invitation to join
them in singing was offered, appearing in robes of
red. for every note they sang it transformed into a
jewel creating a beautiful mosaic of melody.
A candle once lit, kissed the one along, a river of
light flowed and danced down the nave. Guttering
and flickering as breath sang out.
and we waited.

The End

The jarred mind of a poet
Is one that is fragile, helpless and solid
You read, you revise, and you repeat
Certain areas of your existence
Their existence
To grasp an idea that the lightbulb
Will just about stay on for enough time
Desperately trying to grab to gravitate to glorify
An obsidious thought in passing
The lightbulb is not always a bulb
nor electric
a flame, perhaps
a whisper can surely destroy it
Heated, holy, and hungry
Are I and the flame

Something sticky
Something to stay

I have run dry
I have nothing more to say.

Ingram Content Group UK Ltd.
Milton Keynes UK
UKHW020235210623
423745UK00015B/462